This book belongs to

Welcome to my illustrated world of Night Gardens!

Relax and explore a world of engaging pen–and–ink illustrations, all waiting to be brought to life through color. For artists, gardeners, and fantasy lovers of all ages.

The designs are filled with intricate and whimsical pictures to satisfy all skill levels. If you like exploring twilight forests, quiet crafts, and unique ways to unwind, then take an evening amble through these charming pages.

The day has ended, your dreams are waiting…

See more at rjhampson.com

russelljamesart

Published by Hop Skip Jump
PO Box 1324 Buderim Queensland Australia 4556

First published 2022.
Copyright © 2023 R. J. Hampson.

ISBN: 978-1-922472-17-5

Using this book

Find a quiet place away from distractions. Relax and immerse yourself in the process of coloring as you explore the details of each fantastic illustration.

This book is best suited to color pencils or markers. Wet mediums should be used sparingly. Slide a card behind the illustration you are coloring to avoid marker bleed through.

Find fresh coloring pages by signing up to the R.J. Hampson newsletter. Get free downloadable pages and updates on new books at -

rjhampson.com/coloring

HOMEWARD BOUND

FAWN IN BRAMBLES

FOREST CABIN

HANGING GARDENS

DRAGON GATE

MR FOGHERTY BEGINS A LONG JOURNEY

ELVEN HOME

WILD ROSE

ROSE CASTLE

OUT OF EDEN

GRASSLANDS

FIREFLY

BUTTERFLY

NOCTURNE

CHERRY BLOSSOMS

CUCKOO CLOCK

JUNGLE NIGHTS

ROYAL GARDENS

RAPUNZEL

TWILIGHT IN THE MAGNOLIA TREE

FROGS

LARRY VS THE MONSTER FLOWERS

THE GLOAMING

TINY WINDMILL

TROUBLE

Need more coloring treats?

Find new coloring pages by signing up to Russell's newsletter.
Get free downloadable pages and updates on new books at -
rjhampson.com/coloring

Thanks for choosing this coloring book.
If you enjoyed it, please consider leaving a review.
It will help to let more people in on the experience
plus you'd certainly make this illustrator very happy!

Published books in this series

See flip-throughs and new releases at **rjhampson.com**

9 781922 472175

This book belongs to

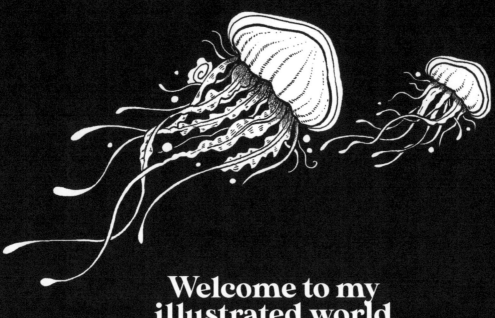

Welcome to my illustrated world of Oceans!

Relax and explore a world of wonderfully engaging and beautifully detailed pen–and–ink illustrations–all waiting to be brought to life through color.
For artists and explorers of all ages.

The artworks in my books are based on illustrations I have drawn over my years as an artist. The designs are filled with intricate and whimsical pictures to satisfy all skill levels.

See more at rjhampson.com

  russelljamesart

Published by Hop Skip Jump
PO Box 1324 Buderim Queensland Australia 4556

First published 2021.
Copyright © 2023 R. J. Hampson.

ISBN: 978-1-922472-25-0

hopskipjump®

Using this book

Find a quiet place away from distractions. Relax and immerse yourself in the process of coloring as you explore the details of each fantastic illustration.

This book is best suited to color pencils or markers. Wet mediums should be used sparingly. Slide a card behind the illustration you are coloring to avoid marker bleed through.

Find fresh coloring pages by signing up to the R.J. Hampson newsletter. Get free downloadable pages and updates on new books at -

rjhampson.com/coloring

JELLYFISH

WATER CAGES

CORAL REEF

LIGHTHOUSE

"WHO'S NEXT?"

WHALE OF A TIME

TREASURE ISLAND

DEADLIEST CATCH

SEAHORSE

UTOPIA

TREASURE HUNTERS

LIGHTHOUSE #2

ISLAND DREAM

LOBSTER

WRONG CHOICE

SUSHI

DREAM HOME

ATLANTIS

ATLANTIS

HELLO

SUBMARINE

SEA TURTLES

SEA CASTLE

BIGGER

HOLIDAY

HOLIDAY

INFINITY WAVE

Discover new worlds!

Find new coloring pages by signing up to Russell's newsletter.
Get free downloadable pages and updates on new books at -

rjhampson.com/coloring

Thanks for choosing this coloring book.
If you enjoyed it, please consider leaving a review.
It will help to let more people in on the experience
plus you'd certainly make this illustrator very happy!

Published books in this series

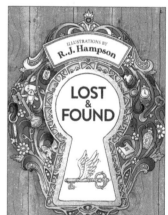

See flip-throughs and new releases at **rjhampson.com**